A Horse for Hanukkah

By Myriam Halberstam

Illustrated by Nancy Cote

Ariella Books

"Good morning, Hannah," whispered Mama.
Hannah slowly opened her eyes.
"Tonight we light the first Hanukkah candle."
"And then we get a present, right?" cried Hannah,
excitedly, as she leapt out of bed.
"Of course, but don't be disappointed if your wish
doesn't come true," Mama winked.

Hannah had been wanting a horse for as long as she
could remember and in the days leading to Hanukkah,
she had pleaded repeatedly with her parents.
"Where would we keep a horse in our apartment?" Mama
would respond. But Hannah could not give up on her wish.

Finally, the time had come: Darkness had arrived;
the shamash candle was lit, and with it, the first candle
of the Festival of Lights. The whole family gathered around.
Hannah especially loved singing *Maos Tzur*. If only her
little brother David didn't always whine so out of tune!
Finally – time to unwrap presents.

Papa opened the door to the next room
and Hannah just about fell over.
Standing there waving its tail was a horse,
a real live horse! "*Shalom*," the horse hummed
in a velvety voice. Hannah couldn't believe
her ears: A horse that speaks, and Hebrew
no less? She was simply overwhelmed
with joy.

"Thank you, Mama, thank you Papa," cried Hannah,
as she danced around the horse with delight.
"I will call you Golda". David was spellbound,
and held out his hand for Golda to sniff.
Golda gently licked it. "Your tongue is rough,"
David giggled.

After a long evening of excitement over the horse, and lots of singing of Hanukkah songs, the children went to bed happy and satisfied. Being Hannah's horse, Golda slept in Hannah's room. Hannah had trouble finding her bed. "That's ok", said Hannah as she squeezed past Golda's belly and tumbled into bed. She thought she had heard a soft, *"Laila Tov"*, Good Night, but she was not sure. Utterly exhausted, she fell asleep.

On the second night of Hanukkah it was
bath time.
Golda was curious. She dipped her nose
into the tub and in one big slurp drank up
all the water.

Hannah and David laughed with delight; they didn't much like taking baths, anyway. But Mama was not at all pleased. "This is not water for you to drink," she advised Golda sternly.

On the third night of Hanukkah, Golda sniffed at the candles. Suddenly she sneezed. With one big *"achoo"* she blew out all three candles and the shamash.

Now that was going too far: "The Hanukkah candles are not to be played with!" complained Papa. "They have to burn out by themselves; you're not allowed to blow them out."

"Yes, we know." Hannah looked quite sad, and so did Golda.

Hannah thought she heard Golda say, *"Ayze broch!"*—What a mess!

On the fourth night of Hanukkah, Grandma and Grandpa joined in the celebration. Grandma brought lots of delicious, homemade latkes. Nobody makes them like Grandma does! Grandpa and Grandma stopped in their tracks when they saw a horse! Golda brayed: *"Na'eem me'od,"* nice to meet you, in Hebrew. Were Grandma and Grandpa hearing things?

Everybody sat down for the latkes dinner.
Golda stood to the side and watched as Mama
served sour cream, applesauce and some lox
with the latkes. Golda ran her tongue over
her lips.

Suddenly there was a huge slurp: with her big tongue, Golda had
scooped up all the latkes off the plate and into her mouth. The bowl with
sour cream tumbled to the floor. Grandma cried: "Oy vey, all my latkes!"
"Ta'eem," delicious, Golda seemed to say. "You beast!" Grandma scolded.
Mama tried to wipe the floor. David whined, "I didn't even get one latke!"
Papa was speechless. Only Golda was happy: munching away at the latkes,
enjoying every moment. Grandma and Grandpa went home, upset.
Mama and Papa ordered pizza.

Hannah tried to explain to Golda that you just didn't behave this way. And that you should ask before you take the last piece of cake—or in this case, the last latke. Golda winked at Hannah lovingly. Hannah heard: *"Sleecha,"* sorry. It's so hard to stay angry at a talking horse!

On the fifth night of Hanukkah, the family was invited
to visit friends. This time, they left Golda alone.
Joyfully the guests danced Israeli folk dances together.
It was late when Hannah, David and their parents
headed home.

Golda had been waiting patiently in Hannah's room. As Hannah dropped into bed, exhausted by all the dancing, she saw that Golda had left her a little present. A huge pile of smelly dung plopped right next to Hannah's pillow! Eew! But Hannah was too tired to do anything about it. She fell asleep, despite the stench under her nose.

On the sixth night of Hanukkah, the Rosenbaum family wanted to play dreidel. Papa handed out chocolate money and peanuts for betting.
David, Hannah and Papa sat in a circle on the floor and spun the dreidel. Golda watched intently.
She wanted to play, too.

Golda tried to spin the dreidel with her hoof.
But hooves are not made for spinning dreidels.
Frustrated, Golda stamped and crushed the wooden
dreidel into many tiny pieces.
"Now, that's the last straw," cried Papa.
And the game was over.

On the seventh night of Hanukkah, Golda behaved
quite well. She stood at the table and politely watched
the family eat. "What a good horse," Mama and Papa
praised her. Hannah stroked her mane.

Suddenly, Golda began to neigh. *"EEEmaawle"*, mother!!
Her tail had accidentally gotten too close to the menorah.
Hannah screamed; Papa tried to pat out the fire. David
dashed into the kitchen, grabbed the fire extinguisher and
sprayed sticky foam everywhere.

The flames were doused. Little David had managed to keep the fire from spreading. What a hero! Golda shivered in fear. The living room had turned into a cotton candy landscape. Mama put her face in her hands and began to cry.

"Good morning, Hannah," whispered mama.
"Wake up, dear: Tonight we light the first Hanukkah candle!"
Hannah rubbed her eyes. "The first? I thought it was the eighth.
We've already lit seven candles!"
Hannah's mama laughed. "You must have been dreaming. Tonight is
the first night of Hanukkah, so of course we light the first candle."
"And then we open presents?" asked Hannah.
"Why of course," answered mama, giving her a kiss.

"I won't be at all disappointed if I don't get a real horse
this year," said Hannah quickly.
"Really? Now that's something new! What happened?"
Mama asked wonderingly.
"Oh, I just grew up over night," Hannah answered,
smiling to herself. "I'm much, much more reasonable now."

American filmmaker *Myriam Halberstam* is also a journalist and author of children's books. She grew up in Germany, has called New York and Tel Aviv her home and now lives in Berlin, Germany with her husband and two daughters. She founded Ariella Books in the Spring of 2010.

Nancy Cote is a National Award Winning Artist who has illustrated over two dozen picture books and has written five of her own. Her work has been featured in many exhibits and collections throughout the U.S. She is a teacher in the C.E. Program at Rhode Island School of Design and lives in Somerset, MA with her family.

The Story of Hanukkah*

The story of Hanukkah happened a long, long time ago in the land of Israel. At that time, the most special place for the Jewish people was the Temple in Jerusalem. Like most synagogues, the Temple contained a holy ark, a cabinet that held the Torah. Above the ark hung the Eternal Light, a special lamp that was meant to shine all day and all night. This light did not need a light bulb or candles; it was lit using oil. Whenever it seemed as if the light was about to go out, the person in charge would pour new oil into the lamp to keep the light burning.

At the time of the Hanukkah story, a mean king named Antiochus ruled over the Jewish people in the land of Israel. "I don't like these Jewish people," declared Antiochus. "They are so different from me. I don't celebrate Shabbat or read from the Torah – so why should they?" Antiochus made many new rules that made the Jewish people very sad. "No more celebrating the Shabbat! No more reading the Torah!" shouted Antiochus. Antiochus told his guards to go into the Temple and make a mess. They broke the ark, smashed the jars of oil that were used to light the Eternal Light and brought mud, dirt, and garbage into the Temple.

Antiochus and his soldiers made the Jews feel sad and angry. A Jewish person named Judah Maccabee said, "We must stop Antiochus! We must think of ways to make him leave the land of Israel." At first, Judah's followers, called the Maccabees, were afraid. "Judah," they said, "Antiochus has so many soldiers. His soldiers carry big weapons and wear armor. He even has huge elephants to fight his battles. How can we Jews, who don't even have weapons, ever fight against him?" Judah said, "If we think very hard and plan very carefully, we will be able to defeat him." It took a long time, but at last the Maccabees chased Antiochus and his men out of Israel.

As soon as Antiochus and his soldiers were gone, the Jewish people ran to Jerusalem to clean their Temple. When they tried to light the Eternal Light, they discovered that Antiochus' soldiers had broken all the jars of oil. They searched and searched, until at last they found one tiny jar of oil – enough to light the lamp for just one day. But it took eight days to make more oil! The Maccabees decided to light the lamp anyway. To their surprise, a miracle occurred and the little jar of oil lasted for eight whole days! The Jewish people could not believe their good fortune. First, their small army had chased away Antiochus' large army, and now the tiny jar of oil had lasted for eight whole days!

The Jewish people prayed and thanked God for these miracles. Every year during Hanukkah, Jews light menorahs for eight days to remember the special miracles that happened long ago.

---

* The transliterated word *Hanukkah* can be spelled in a number of different ways – including *Channukah, Chanuka,* etc.